BEDTIME STORIES

Uncle Arthur''s Best

2

Illustrations by Annette Agard

ISBN 0-904748-95-2
5-vol. set 0-904748-99-5

Printed and published by
The Stanborough Press Ltd.
Alma Park, Grantham, Lincs., NG31 9SL
England

CONTENTS

Johnnie's little jokes

Johnnie was big for his age. And, if we are to tell the whole truth, it must also be said that . . . er, let's just say that Johnnie enjoyed eating. OK? Oh, yes. And he was full of mischief.

He was always thinking of ways of annoying people, just to see them cross. He called them his 'little jokes'.

Johnnie made the mistake of trying one out on his mother. This is always a dangerous thing to do.

It happened like this.

One day, just before lunch, his mother left the meal in the cooker and went out into the garden to hang clothes on the washing line. While she was gone Johnnie closed the door quietly and bolted it. Then he locked the front door so that Mother couldn't get in that way, and waited to see what would happen.

Well, a lot happened.

When his mother had hung all the clothes on the line, she returned to the kitchen door and found it shut. Then she noticed that it was bolted.

'Strange!' she thought. 'How could that have happened?'

Then she remembered Johnnie and his 'jokes', and she began to bang on the door.

Johnnie chuckled. The banging grew louder.

'Open the door, Johnnie!'

No answer.

'Do you hear me? Open the door!'

Still no answer.

Then, as Mother smelled the lunch burning in the cooker, she became frantic.

'Johnnie! Do you hear me? Open the door. The lunch is burning! Open the door!'

Still Johnnie kept quiet, but he was beginning to get worried. His little joke wasn't working out too well.

'Wait till I catch you, Johnnie,' cried Mother. 'I'll punish you for this. Open the door!'

Johnnie knew now that he had made his mother very cross. He was, in fact, in a very bad fix. If only he had been *outside* instead of *inside*, he might have stood a chance of getting away. Now he was trapped. What was he to do?

Deciding it was about time to open the door, Johnnie got a stick and, standing on the bottom stair, reached over and pushed back the bolt. Then he dropped the stick and ran for dear life upstairs.

But Mother was after him. Right on his trail. Forgetting the burning dinner, she bounded up the stairs as fast as Johnnie, and maybe even a little faster.

Johnnie heard her coming and dashed into a bedroom, seeking a way of escape. The window was open. He took one look outside, then jumped.

At this moment Mother reached the bedroom door — just in time to see Johnnie disappear. She went over to the window, but didn't dare look out. It was nearly twenty feet to the ground.

Nearby was a picket fence. She couldn't bear the thought of what she might see down below.

At last, hearing no cry of pain, she plucked up the courage and looked. And what do you suppose she saw?

There was Johnnie grinning at her from behind an apple tree.

'A-ha,' he cried, laughing. 'You didn't catch me, did you?'

'Just you wait!' cried his mother.

He waited. In fact, they both waited. And Mother knew she was bound to win. Mothers always win.

You see, it was lunchtime, and she knew that although Johnnie liked to play jokes, he also liked to eat. Very much so. It was not likely that he would stay away very long when it was time to eat. Mother guessed right.

Now that his little 'joke' was over and his tummy told him it was lunchtime, Johnnie began to think that it would be a very wise thing to make peace with Mother at the earliest possible moment.

Soon he started walking towards the kitchen door. He hoped he would be able to 'get away with it' by his usual winning smile and just saying he was sorry.

He was wrong. His 'little joke' had not only got *him* into trouble. It had got the lunch in the cooker into even more serious trouble.

The plates were set out on the table. Johnnie took his usual seat. Then, without delay, Mother served up on his plate what was left of the lunch cooking in the oven.

It was burnt to a cinder.

'How did it get like that?' asked Johnnie, puzzled.

'It got like that while I was locked outside and you wouldn't let me in,' said Mother. 'There's a little joke for you. Your lunch looks like a mixture of coal and charcoal.'

His mother didn't have to insist that Johnnie ate it. It would have been impossible anyway.

But Johnnie had been hit where it hurt most: his tummy.

It seemed a long, long time until tea-time. Johnnie's tummy rumbled and rumbled. He had a lot of time to think that playing 'little jokes' isn't always such a good idea after all.

Boys in a bonfire

'Can't we do something exciting tonight?' said Ben.

'Yes, let's!' said Lee. 'But what can we do? Everything's so *boring* round here.'

'Let's have a bonfire!' suggested another boy.

'Brilliant idea,' said Ben. 'But where?'

'In Lee's garden,' said someone.

'How about it, Lee?' asked Ben.

'Should be OK,' said Lee. 'Grandma's going out tonight. But I'll have to sweep up some of the straw that's lying around or we might set the house on fire!'

'Tell you what, *you* sweep up the straw. The rest of us will bring the wood,' said Ben. 'How does that sound?' he asked the boys.

'Suits us fine,' they said. 'We'll be round about nine o'clock.'

At seven o'clock that night Lee took a brush and started to sweep his back garden. Needless to say, his grandma, with whom he lived, was very surprised. She had never known Lee to be that fond of work.

'What's going on?' she asked. 'Why are you sweeping up the straw at this time of night?'

'For the fun of it!' said Lee.

'It's getting dark. I think you'd better come in,' said Grandma. 'You'll do a better job in the morning when you can see.'

'Aw, Gran!' grumbled Lee. 'I *feel* like sweeping. Can't I sweep if I want to?'

'Indoors!' said Grandma. 'Put that broom away!'

Lee obeyed. But not for long.

A few minutes later Grandma went to a meeting at her church. She told Lee to stay indoors and read quietly. She would be home soon. Hardly had she left than Lee seized the brush and went on with his sweeping.

At nine o'clock the other boys turned up, all carrying armfuls of wood which they had gathered from one place or another. Soon they had built a big bonfire and Lee got a thrill setting it alight.

As the flames roared upwards, the boys ran around the fire yelling wildly in their excitement.

'Let's play jumping the bonfire,' cried someone.

'Right!' said the others. 'Who'll be first?'

'I will!' 'I will!' said one after another.

Of course, everybody couldn't be first, so they decided to let Ben lead, with Lee bringing up the rear.

Taking a long run, Ben jumped. Over he went, the others following.

'Your turn, Lee!' they all cried, as they watched him ready to jump.

Lee ran — and jumped. But he didn't make it to the other side. . . .

For some reason, Ben got the idea that he was to start to jump back over the fire. So, just as Lee jumped, Ben jumped. The two boys met in the middle of the fire, crashing into one another.

Down they went into the flames, while everybody screamed in fright.

Ben managed to get out quickly. Poor Lee appeared to be stunned by the bump he got when he collided with Ben. He didn't seem to know what he was doing and rolled this way and that in the fire until a neighbour rushed up and dragged him out.

Just then Grandma returned. When she saw the fire she guessed at once why Lee had been sweeping the garden earlier that evening.

At first she was very angry, but her anger melted when she saw how horribly burned poor Lee was. He was taken to hospital to have his burns dressed and was kept in for several days.

It was six months before Lee was well enough to go outdoors and play with his friends again — six months of pain and misery.

When telling me this story Lee said he learned two lessons that night. He will never try to deceive his grandmother again — or play with fire!

Kylie's gift

'Dana,' said Kylie lovingly, as she laid her doll in its red pram and carefully tucked the covers around it. 'I'm sure there is not another doll in all the world as lovely as you are.'

Dana did not reply, but laid herself back on the white pillowcase, and closed her eyes as if perfectly happy.

'I think we'll go for a walk, now, Dana,' said Kylie. Pulling the garden gate behind her, she went down the street pushing her doll's pram. (Kylie had not asked her parent's permission. Children should never go out without a grown-up.)

'Dana,' said Kylie sternly, 'I do hope you behave yourself while we are in town. And, if you cry, don't expect to get any sweets!'

Needless to say, Dana didn't cry and, indeed, behaved better than most babies do!

17

Kylie enjoyed the walk, feeling very proud of herself, as little girls do when they go out with a doll's pram.

When she reached the end of the street, Kylie met a poor little girl carrying the dirtiest, raggiest doll you ever saw.

'Dana,' whispered Kylie, 'I'm so glad you're not as dirty as that.'

But the little girl seemed to love her dirty, ragged doll just as much as Kylie loved Dana. She was hugging it very tightly and telling it that it was just the loveliest doll in all the world.

At this moment, just as the little girl started to cross the road, a car swung round the corner. The little girl jumped back and saved herself, but in her fright she let go of her precious doll. It rolled away, underneath the car and was crushed to pieces.

The little girl burst into tears as she saw her precious doll. It was the only one she had ever had.

Kylie's loving little heart was touched immediately. What could she do? Nobody was about, and it seemed that it was up to her to comfort the little girl. Running to her side, she put her hand on her shoulder and told her not to cry. But she cried anyway.

Kylie looked at her pram and thought of her beloved Dana. Could she? Could she?

'What's your name?' Kylie asked the little girl.

'Lucy,' the little girl replied between sobs.

'Lucy,' said Kylie, 'don't cry any more. You can

have Dana. She's the beautifullest doll in all the world, and she'll make you happy again.'

Giving Dana one last hug and kiss, she handed her over to Lucy, who could scarcely believe her eyes.

'For me?' she said, 'for me?'

'Yes,' said Kylie, 'for keeps.' And Kylie turned away and ran back home as fast as she could push her pram, in case she changed her mind. Then she sat down on the front doorstep and thought of what had happened. She looked tearfully into the empty pram.

But somebody had seen what had happened.

High up in one of the nearby houses, a lady had been looking out of the window. She had heard the screech of the car wheels as it rounded the corner. Seen the doll smashed. And then, to her amazement, she had watched Kylie's kind act.

A few days later that same lady called at Kylie's house with a long, brown paper parcel in her arms. She said it was a new baby for a kind girl who had given her own away.

Kylie was so happy she didn't know what to do. She just kept saying, 'Thank you, thank you.'

Kylie called her new doll Dana, to remind her of the one she had loved so much and given away. But when she thought about it she realized that the best moment of all was not receiving a new doll from a kind lady. It was the moment when she had handed over the other one to the little girl near the street corner.

Faithful and true

Ted Mix stopped his car on a lonely road in California to let his dog out for a walk.

A few minutes later he called his dog. He wanted to continue the journey without delay. But the dog refused to come. Instead, it stood at the edge of the canyon and barked.

'That's odd,' said Ted. 'That dog always obeys me. There must be something very interesting down in that canyon.'

He went over to see for himself.

Suddenly, as the dog stopped barking for a moment, he heard another bark from far down the canyon. It was weak and faint, but a bark just the same. There was no mistaking it. Somewhere down in that deep, dark canyon there was a dog in trouble.

'Must be caught in a trap,' Ted said.

Slowly and carefully he made his way down the steep slope, wondering what he would find.

As he went down the dog's barking grew louder and fiercer. Ted knew now the barking didn't come from a dog that was trapped but rather a dog that was guarding something.

At last, as he looked this way and that, Ted caught his first glimpse of the dog. It was a little terrier, barking so furiously that he was afraid to go near it.

But why was it barking like this in such a place? What could it be guarding so faithfully?

Then he saw what it was. Beside the dog was a man lying on the ground. He seemed to be asleep, and was bleeding. Beyond the man was the wreck of a car.

Ted soon worked out what had happened. There had been a car accident. The car had tumbled down the slope of the canyon. Somehow the man and the little mongrel dog had been thrown free. The man was hurt and unconscious. The dog was not. Later on Ted discovered that the accident had happened hours before.

What could he do now? He decided to climb up the canyon and get back into his own car. He would have gladly taken the man, but he was too heavy to carry. He would gladly have taken the dog, but the little mongrel would not leave his injured master.

Ted drove on to the nearest town and told the police what he had found. Police and ambulance men returned to the spot with stretchers and ropes.

As the police and ambulance men climbed down towards the wreck, the little dog set up another furious burst of barking and tried its best to keep the men from touching his injured master. They had to drive it off before they could tie the man's injured body on to the stretcher. In time the injured man was hauled up to the rim of the canyon — and was on his way to hospital in the ambulance, sirens blaring, lights flashing.

Until the ambulance drove off the dog circled round and round, barking for all he was worth. Finally Ted caught the little creature, wrapped it in a jacket, and carried it to his car. Only then did it quieten down, as though it knew that its job was done and there was no need to bark any more.

When the injured man regained consciousness in hospital the police were able to tell him what had happened.

Every newspaper for miles carried pictures of that little dog and the story of its faithfulness.

Soon all California was talking about the brave little dog. Hundreds of people offered it a home. Ted would willingly have kept it.

After a long time in hospital, however, the man got better. When he went home Ted made sure that he was reunited with his faithful little dog.

The little dog had saved the life of his master by staying faithful and true at its post.

It *does* pay to be polite

How old should a boy be before he begins to be polite? Ten, would you say? Or 9, 8, 7, 6, 5 or 4?

Dick learned to be polite when he was very, very young. From the time he first learned to talk, his mother taught him to say, 'Please', 'Thank you', and 'Excuse me', and 'I'm sorry', and 'You're welcome' — and other words which help such a lot to make life pleasant.

One day when Dick was not quite 5 years old he got on a bus with his mother. He was ahead, with Mother following, as they walked down the aisle looking for a seat.

The bus moved forward with a sudden jerk. Dick stumbled. As he did so he stepped on a man's foot. The man pulled his foot away, and looked upset.

'I'm sorry, Sir,' said Dick. 'I'm very sorry; I didn't mean to.'

The man smiled. So did all the other passengers. Everybody was surprised — and pleased — to hear a little boy speak so politely.

Smiling at Mother, the stranger began to ask Dick some questions.

'What's your name?'

'Dick Gentry, Sir.'

'How old are you?'

'Four — but I'll soon be 5.'

'When's your birthday?'

Dick told him.

'Where do you live?'

Dick gave the man his address.

Meanwhile all the people on the bus were watching and listening. There was a smile on every face because one little boy was so friendly and, above all, so very polite.

A few weeks passed. Dick became 5 years old. On his birthday, to his great surprise, he received an unexpected present. It had a note inside saying: 'From your friend on the bus.' But there was no name or address, so Dick couldn't write and thank him.

Believe it or not, Dick received a present on his birthday from the same man *every year* until he was 18 years of age.

When he left grammar school he received an

expensive camera with the same words, 'From your friend on the bus'.

All this time he had no idea who his friend could be, but he always remembered the accident on the bus when he was a little boy. Then came a very cold winter. In those days almost everyone had coal fires for heating. So when coal supplies ran out it meant that the poorer people were going to be very, very cold.

Coal was delivered in bags on carts pulled by horses. In normal times coal carts were a familiar sight in the streets. But when coal supplies ran out coal carts stopped running. There was no more coal to deliver.

Dick was worried. His home was like an ice box. There was no coal for the fire. Father and Mother were not well and Grandma, aged 90, was in serious danger.

Dick phoned the coal company. 'This is serious,' he said. 'We're freezing. My parents are ill, and my grandmother is in real danger. Can't you send us some coal?'

'Sorry,' said the man at the coal company. 'There's so little coal left that we're not sending the carts out till Monday morning.'

'Till Monday morning!' cried Dick. 'My parents can't stand it till then. It might be too late for my grandmother. Can't you do something for us, please?'

'I'm sorry,' said the man. 'By the way, what is your name?'

'My name is Dick; Dick Gentry. Please help us if you can.'

'I'll see what I can do,' said the man.

An hour or so later a beautiful car stopped at Dick's house. A chauffeur stepped out and approached the door. Dick went out to see what he wanted.

'Is this where Dick Gentry lives?' he asked.

'Yes,' said Dick. 'Is there something I can do for you?'

'No,' said the chauffeur. 'I've brought you something.'

To Dick's astonishment the chauffeur hauled six sacks of coal out of the boot of that beautiful car.

'Are these for us?' said Dick.

'Yes,' said the chauffeur.

'Oh, thank you!' cried Dick. 'Thank you very, very much! But who sent them?'

'There's a note in one of the sacks,' said the chauffeur, as he said goodbye and drove away.

Dick tore open the sacks. Inside one of them he found a note. It read: 'From your friend on the bus.'

He could hardly believe his eyes. Then he guessed. The man on the bus must be the chairman of the coal company!

Dick was right.

And all these kindnesses had come because a little boy had been polite years and years ago.

Hand in the dark

Natasha, who lives in Natal, is a rosy-cheeked, bright-eyed little girl about 4 years old.

Of course, she loves her mother. And I believe she loves her daddy a teeny bit too, I believe this because I happen to know how happy she is when he comes home from work each evening.

After Daddy comes home, Natasha plays with him for a short time — and then she has to go to bed.

All day long she waits for Daddy's homecoming. Time and again she asks Mummy: 'Is Daddy coming home soon? Will he be much longer?'

Then at last, when the time comes, she goes running down the lane to meet him.

There's a special place where they always meet, a quiet, pretty spot in the country lane that goes past their home. Natasha would rather miss her supper than not be there when Daddy comes walking up the hill from work.

One day Daddy phoned Mummy to say that he would be back late, and to tell Natasha not to meet him at the usual place this time.

But when Natasha heard about it she was very upset.

'Of course, I'll have to go,' she said. 'Daddy will be expecting me.'

'But Daddy has just said he won't expect you this time,' said Mummy.

'Oh, but he will,' said Natasha. 'I'm sure he will.'

'It will be dark when he comes.'

'Then I'll go and meet him in the dark.'

Mummy smiled. She was sure Natasha would change her mind when the sun went down.

But she didn't.

Evening came. Darkness began to fall.

'I think it's nearly bedtime,' said Mummy.

'Oh, but I must go and meet daddy,' said Natasha.

'You can't go down the lane in the dark alone.'

'I could,' said Natasha. 'I won't mind. And Daddy will be looking for me.'

In many countries, of course, it would be unsafe for a little girl to go out alone — especially in the dark. Mothers have to be strict about that, but where Natasha lives it is quite safe.

Soon it became very dark; dark enough to make most little girls afraid of going out of the house alone.

Mother opened the front door and let Natasha look out into the night.

'Do you still want to go and meet Daddy?' she asked.

'Yes,' said Natasha. 'Of course I do.'

'All right,' said Mummy. 'You can go. Put your coat on. It's cold out there.'

Natasha put on her coat and took the torch Mummy handed her. Then the two went down to the gate together.

'Bye, darling,' said Mummy, as Natasha waved her hand and disappeared into the darkness. 'Be careful. Don't fall over.'

'I'll be careful,' said Natasha, and trotted off down the lane.

Mummy stood at the gate and watched the little point of light bobbing about in the dark as Natasha toddled on towards the meeting place.

By and by, from far in the distance, Mother heard a little voice cry, 'Hello, Daddy!' Then a big deep voice replied: 'Whatever are you doing here at this time of night, you little scamp!' Then Mummy knew everything was all right.

When Natasha and Daddy got home, Mummy said: 'But Natasha, weren't you frightened when you walked in the dark all by yourself?'

'Oh, no,' said Natasha. 'I wasn't a bit frightened. You see, Jesus held my hand and went with me all the way.'

What wonderful faith!

Jesus will hold your hand in the dark, too, if you ask Him.

Grandad's camera

Somewhere on the coast of Cornwall, and near a sandy beach, lived a special family. The family was made up of Grandad, Grandma, Mother, Martin and Paul.

Living in such a beautiful place, they often went for picnics. One summer day, when the sun was shining, the wind was warm, and the sea was smooth, the family did just that.

Everybody was happy — until something happened.

Grandad, you see, liked to take pictures with his expensive camera. To take especially nice pictures, he carried an extra lens with him.

Eager to go into the water, Grandad asked Mother to look after the camera and extra lens. She said she would. So Grandad, Grandma, Paul and Martin went off to paddle.

After a while little Martin came back.

'I want my bucket and spade,' he said. 'Where are they?'

Mother stood up, handed Martin his bucket and spade, and sat down again.

Then she noticed she no longer had Grandad's precious lens. . . .

Alarmed, she got up again, moved her chair, looked in the lunch baskets and shook the rug; but there was no lens anywhere. She began scraping the sand with her hands, but it was useless. The lens had disappeared.

Grandad came up from the water to get his camera. 'What's the matter?' he asked. 'Lost something?'

'Yes,' said Mother. 'The lens.'

'Not my special lens!' cried Grandad. 'And it cost *such* a lot of money! Whatever did you do with it?'

'I don't know,' said Mother. 'I had it in my hand a few minutes ago. But I got up to give Martin his bucket and spade and the next thing I knew there was no lens. It just vanished. Surely it can't be far away — unless Martin took it off with him.'

Martin was called over, but he couldn't remember ever having seen the lens.

Then the search really began. Grandad, Grandma, Mother, Paul and Martin looked everywhere. They turned everything upside down. They dug in the sand, inch by inch, all around the place where Mother had been sitting. But no lens turned up.

Then Grandad had a bright idea. He went to the

beach attendant who lent him a large sieve. With this he began sifting the sand, shovelful by shovelful, till he was tired out.

'I'm afraid it's hopeless,' he said. 'Too bad. But why spoil the day? Let's have lunch.'

Everybody thought this was a good idea, especially Paul and Martin. Afterwards Grandad and Grandma, Paul and Martin went paddling again. Mother stayed behind and went on searching and searching. She couldn't bear to think of Grandad losing something he valued so much.

Then she saw it, a little gleam of light reflected from the sun. It was coming from something buried just a quarter of an inch or so down in the sand.

She caught her breath. Could it be? 'Oh, dear Lord,' she whispered, 'Please make it Grandad's lens!'

It was.

'I've found it!' she shouted, loud enough for everybody on the beach to hear.

All the family came running. Grandad, Grandma, Paul and Martin.

You should have seen the joy on Grandad's face!

'I was praying you'd find it,' he said.

'So was I,' said Grandma.

'So was I,' said Martin.

'So was I,' said Paul.

'I'm sure we were all praying,' said Mother. 'And how thankful I am that it's found at last.'

Now, don't get the wrong idea. God is not just a big

slot machine in the sky who delivers the goods when a prayer is pushed in.

But He *does* answer prayer. His answer may be 'Yes', 'No', or 'Wait'.

In the case of Grandad's lens, the family didn't have to wait very long!

Who made that noise?

Jane felt all grown up. Mrs. Baldwin, the lady next door, had asked her if she would act as baby-sitter for her two little boys.

It was great to feel trusted like this and she was sure there wouldn't be any trouble, not with little boys like Richard and Daniel.

After supper Jane walked around to Mrs. Baldwin's house, almost bursting with pride. This was her very first job outside her own home. Tonight she would be 'in charge' of two little boys who would have to do what she told them. She had never felt so important in all her life.

Mrs. Baldwin welcomed her and showed her to the bedroom where Richard and Daniel were already in bed, though not asleep.

'I told them to be very good while I'm out,' said Mrs. Baldwin, 'and I'm sure they will be.'

'I'm sure they will,' said Jane, smiling happily at the two boys. 'I'll read them a story and that will send them off to sleep.'

'Good!' cried the two boys, kicking up the bedclothes.

'That will be fine,' said Mrs. Baldwin. 'I'm sure everything will be all right. I won't be back late.'

Then she was gone.

Jane read a story, then another and another, until the two lively boys gradually became sleepier and sleepier. At last they shut their eyes and were off to dreamland.

Jane put the book down and wondered what she should do next.

It was then that she heard the noise.

At first it was just a scratching sound, but soon it grew louder and louder, as though someone was treading on a squeaky floorboard in the next room.

Jane's eyes almost popped out with fright. Was somebody trying to break into the house? Could it be a burglar? Or someone come to kidnap the boys while Mrs. Baldwin was out?

Her face turned white. Her throat went dry. She couldn't swallow. She couldn't speak. She couldn't even cry out.

Still the noise went on. It seemed to be getting nearer and nearer.

Squeak! squeak! went the noise followed by a loud rustling sound.

This was too much for Jane. All her self-importance had gone. She knew now she was just a child after all. Suddenly she let out a scream that must have been heard a mile away.

The boys woke up.

'What's the matter?' they cried, sitting up in bed. Seeing Jane's frightened face they became scared too.

'The noise!' whispered Jane. 'Can't you hear it?'

The boys didn't want to hear it. They dived under the bedclothes.

Just then there were real footsteps outside and a familiar voice called: 'Are you all right, Jane?' It was Mother.

'Y-y-y-y-y-es,' stammered Jane as she opened the front door. 'It was just the noise. It frightened me.'

'What noise?' said Mother. 'I can't hear any noise.'

'Just listen!' said Jane.

Mother sat down and listened. But there was no noise. The house was silent except for the ticking of the clock and the deep breathing of the two boys who were just going back to sleep again.

'You must have been imagining things,' said Mother. 'If you're going to be a babysitter you mustn't let yourself get upset over little things. If you do feel frightened say your prayers. That will make you feel better.'

Then Mother left.

Ten minutes later Jane heard the noise again.

She was about to let out another scream when she remembered Mother's advice. Falling on her knees she poured out her heart to God.

'Please save us from the bad man who's trying to get into the house!' she cried. 'Don't let him hurt me. And don't let him kidnap Richard and Daniel. And please help me not to be frightened of him.'

God must have been smiling when He heard that prayer.

How long Jane stayed on her knees I don't know. But suddenly she heard the sound of a car driving into the garage. 'It must be Mrs. Baldwin,' she told herself.

Jumping up she ran to the front door and opened it.

'How's my babysitter?' asked Mrs. Baldwin. 'Everything go all right?'

'Oh, yes, quite all right,' said Jane. 'That is, all except the noise.'

'What noise?'

'Oh, it was dreadful!' said Jane. 'I was afraid somebody was coming to kidnap the boys.'

'What sort of noise?' said a worried Mrs. Baldwin.

'Well, it was a sort of squeaky, rustling sound. I don't know how else to describe it.'

'Oh!' cried Mrs. Baldwin, with a loud laugh. 'That's our guinea-pigs. I should have told you about them. They do make an awful noise some nights.'

'Guinea-pigs!' said Jane. 'And to think I was so scared.'

William's long walk

William was in one of his very difficult moods. He didn't like this and he didn't like that. And he didn't want to do anything that anybody else wanted to do.

The worst came one afternoon when Dad said he was planning to take all the family into town. Mum was delighted, and so were William's brothers and sisters. But not William. He said he didn't want to go. He would rather stay at home.

William lived in the days when people travelled either on horseback or in wagons drawn by horses. You would think that the promise of a twenty-mile ride in a wagon behind a team of horses would have made everybody happy, but William was just difficult.

For a while he sat there pouting. 'What's the matter?' asked Dad.

'Nothing,' snapped William.

44

'Anything you want?'

'I want to get out and walk.'

'Walk!' cried Dad. 'You couldn't *walk* to town.'

'Yes, I could,' growled William. 'I want to walk.'

'Hey! Steady on there!' said Dad. 'You'd be making a big mistake. Cheer up and enjoy yourself.'

'Don't want to enjoy myself,' said William. 'I want to get out and walk.'

Mile after mile the wagon rolled on, but William didn't change his tune. Over and over he kept muttering, 'I want to get out and walk.'

At last Dad decided he could take no more. Reining in the horses, he brought the wagon to a halt.

'All right, William,' he said. 'If you want to walk so badly, you had better walk.'

William got to his feet at once, climbed out of the wagon, and jumped down on to the road.

Dad started the horses again and the wagon moved slowly on, with William following behind, looking not a bit happier now that he had got his own way.

At first he walked quite quickly, to keep up with the wagon, but after a while his pace grew slower and slower.

Gradually the wagon pulled ahead. By and by William was 100 yards behind. Then 200. Then a quarter of a mile. Then half a mile.

When he looked ahead the wagon seemed to be getting smaller and smaller, but he didn't care. He was on his own. He didn't want to be with the others. He would rather walk anyway.

Next time he looked he could scarcely see the wagon at all.

Suddenly he began to feel lonely. There wasn't a soul in sight. Not even an animal. He couldn't see a house or a barn.

He looked ahead again. The wagon had disappeared! He was all alone in the world. Left behind!

He began to panic and then to run.

'Stop!' he cried. 'Stop! Stop! Stop!'

Though he ran as fast as his legs would carry him, he couldn't even catch sight of the wagon again.

Now he was tired. He couldn't run any more. He couldn't walk any more. So he flung himself down on the ground, and sobbed.

How long he stayed like that I don't know. But to William it seemed ages and ages.

Then he heard footsteps. Looking up, whom do you suppose he saw?

Dad, of course!

Never in his life had he been so glad to see Dad's face. Dad had come back for him! Good old Dad!

'Come on, Son,' said Dad, picking him up in his arms. 'You must be tired by now. How about a ride?'

William didn't need a second invitation. Eagerly he climbed back in the wagon. There was a smile on his face now, and the grumbles were gone. I'm told he wasn't disagreeable again for a long, long time.

Bonfire night

This delightful story was sent to me by a little girl who lives near Birmingham. It's about something that happened on Bonfire Night.

You know what *that* is. Every English boy and girl around the world knows that on 5 November most people light a bonfire and set off fireworks. Most of them have forgotten why and wonder what a fellow called Guy Fawkes has to do with it. But it's a lot of fun anyway.

Perhaps I should say it's fun for boys and girls. Not for dogs and cats. I remember how our dog used to go off somewhere and whine whenever the fireworks began to go off. He didn't like the noise one bit.

And that, I'm sure, is what happened to Jackie's cat, Tibb. As the fun began and the crackers exploded, he vanished. In fact he leapt into the darkness like a shot out of a gun.

When the party was over, the fireworks had all been set off, and the fire had died down, Jackie called and called Tibb to come back, but he didn't come. Tibb was miles away, as far as he could run from those dreadful noises.

When bedtime came and there was no sign of Tibb, Jackie became worried. She wished she hadn't had a bonfire night. Better no fireworks, she thought, than lose her precious Tibb.

Such thoughts didn't help, of course. Tibb did not return. After a while Jackie began to cry. And she shed more tears after she got into bed. Poor Tibb! Out in the cold! All alone! Maybe unable to find his way home!

Then she got an idea.

What happened next she told me in a letter:

'Lying in bed I suddenly remembered BEDTIME STORIES and how children have been helped by Jesus. So I prayed and prayed, "Lord Jesus, You know where Tibb is. Please bring him back to me." '

How about that? A little girl praying for her cat!

But listen. Jackie's letter goes on:

'You may think this was a silly thing to do, but Tibb is very dear to me.

'Well, after a troubled night I awoke in the morning feeling very sad. Again I prayed, "Dear Jesus, If you find Tibb not hurt or frightened by the fireworks, and bring him home again, I will write and tell Uncle Arthur all about it."

'Then I got dressed and went downstairs. I found Mother in the kitchen. As I spoke to her I heard the sound of mewing and rushed to the back door. When I opened it, there was Tibb waiting to come in. Isn't that wonderful?'

Yes, Jackie, it certainly is. But your last line is the best of all.

This is what she wrote:

'Uncle Arthur, I went straight down town and bought an airmail letter so I could write to you. And every step I took my heart was saying, Thank You.'

Tremendous! Every step a Thank You for an answered prayer. That's how all of us should walk every day.

Linda's 'sneakers'

At half past ten one Thursday morning Linda became the proud owner a new pair of trainers. At three o'clock that same day she lost them — or one of them, to be exact.

I should explain that these were tennis shoes or 'sneakers', as some children called them. You know the sort. You can walk so quietly in them that you can sneak up on anybody and they don't know you're coming. Anyway, Linda was overjoyed when Mother bought her a new pair. She wanted to wear them right away.

When they got home from town Linda asked Mother if she and her friend Natasha could go for a little walk to watch the men who were building a new road down by the river. Her mother said yes, on one condition.

'What's that?' asked Linda.

'That you don't go near the river.'

'I wasn't going to go near the river,' said Linda.

'All right,' said her mother. 'You can go; but if you go near the river I'll be sure to find out and then there'll be trouble!'

'Why are you so worried about the river?' asked Linda. 'We often paddle in it in the summer.'

'But it isn't summer,' said her mother. 'The water's much too cold and, what's more, you should always have an older person with you in case you fall in.'

'Don't worry,' said Linda. 'We won't go near it,' though she didn't know then what Natasha might want to do.

As it turned out, Natasha had one purpose in mind. She wanted to go to the river. Linda told her she had promised her mother that she wouldn't go; that she was wearing her new sneakers so she couldn't go; but she went anyway.

Natasha said that everything would be fine. Her mother didn't want her to go to the river, but what of it? The two mothers would never find out.

So that's where they went. Naturally, the first thing they did was take off their shoes and socks and start to paddle.

That's when Linda discovered that Mother was right on one point at least. The water *was* cold. Terribly cold. It just about froze her feet. She decided to put on her socks and shoes again.

Well, she got her socks on again all right, and one

shoe. But when she reached for the other she knocked it off the bank and into the water.

'My shoe!' she cried. 'My lovely new sneaker! Look, Natasha, it's floating away.'

It was indeed. It had fallen in the water right side up and, like a little boat, was floating downstream towards the bridge.

'If we run fast,' said Natasha, 'we might be able to reach it from the bank near the bridge — it's narrower there.'

They ran as hard as they could, but by the time they reached the bridge the shoe had filled with water and sunk. They could see it on the bottom under the bridge.

'What shall I do?' wailed Linda.

'You'll have to go home without it,' said Natasha.

So Linda walked home with one foot in a shoe, the other in a sock. It was *not* comfortable! Neither were her thoughts. On the way the two girls made up a story about how the sneaker had been lost in some long, wet grass in a swamp.

Mother was not taken in. Nor was she pleased.

'To think that I bought you those shoes this very morning!' she said. 'And you've lost one of them already! You can put on a pair of old shoes and go straight back and look for it.'

They ran, planning to ask one of the workmen to go into the water and get the sneaker for them. But the workmen had gone, and — horrors — so had the

shoe. The current had swept it onward, and who could tell where it was now?

They searched both sides of the river without finding it. They saw Linda's father coming in search of them. When he found them by the river the whole truth had to come out. Now, not only both mothers, but both fathers were upset, and that can mean an awful lot of trouble, as you probably know. For one thing, Linda was told that she would have to save every penny of her pocket money for weeks to come to pay for a new pair of shoes. In her letter to me she says: 'I still haven't saved enough yet.'

What an expensive thing it is to disobey and tell lies!

How Mum learned to drive

Mum wanted to drive a car; she planned to drive; she hoped to drive some day. But she never quite got around to it.

The fact is, she was scared of the traffic, scared of the big main road, and most of all scared of the driving test.

All of which was a great nuisance — to her and everybody else. For one thing she couldn't take Vicky to school. A neighbour had to do that. For another, she couldn't go shopping until Dad came home in the evening. She couldn't go anywhere on her own. Somebody always had to take her.

Five-year-old Vicky didn't like it a bit. All her friends had mothers who could drive. Why couldn't *her* mother? What a good time they could have together if only Mother could drive!

Then came an unforgettable day.

'I have a secret to tell you,' said Mother, when Vicky came home from school.

Vicky loved secrets, but this time she was concerned. Mother looked so pale and worried.

'Am I going to have a baby brother?' she asked.

'No, not that,' smiled her mother. 'Something quite different! You won't tell anybody, will you?'

'Of course not,' said Vicky. 'But what is it?'

'Tomorrow', said Mother, 'I'm going to take my driving test.'

Vicky wasn't quite sure what this meant, but Mum explained and she understood that it was something very important.

'I'll never pass,' said Mother. 'I know I won't. That's why I've been taking lessons secretly. I don't want you to tell anybody.'

'You'll pass!' cried Vicky. 'Of course you will! You've had lessons!'

'That's what worries me,' said her mother. 'I'm sure I'm going to fail and that will be awful, especially if everybody heard about it.'

That's when Vicky had a bright idea.

'Can I tell just one person?' she asked.

'Who's that?' asked Mother.

'Rosy,' said Vicky. 'She's my very best friend.'

'Why do you want to tell Rosy?'

'I've just had an idea,' said Vicky.

'What is it?' asked her mother. 'You'd better tell me.'

Vicky was quiet for a few moments.

'All right, I'll tell you,' she said. 'Tomorrow, when you go for your test, Rosy and I will pray that you won't be scared and that you'll pass.'

'What a lovely thought!' said her mother. 'That makes me feel better already.'

The next day came. So did the test.

Mum took Vicky over to Rosy's house to play till she got back.

As Mother left home two little girls knelt down to pray. And they kept on praying until Mother returned.

'Did you pass?' asked Vicky, as Mother walked through the front door.

'I did,' said Mother.

'Goodie, goodie!' cried Vicky. 'I knew you would. We prayed and prayed that you would.'